AFTERLI[

A Company You Can [

The afterlife is under new management...

For con-artist Jack Fortune, death was just another step up the corporate ladder. As CEO of the newly-formed AFTERLIFE INC. Jack's bold vision and winning charm have helped craft an afterlife in which everyone owns a share. Heaven is finally in the hands of the people; quality of death has never been higher.

But all is not right in Paradise. As AFTERLIFE INC. grows in power, so too does opposition to its rule. Not everyone agrees with Jack's style of management, and for a company on the edge of the impossible, threats can come from the unlikeliest of sources.

Business may be booming but Jack's troubles are only just beginning...

Afterlife Inc. created by Jon Lock

NEAR LIFE AND OTHER STORIES
Written by Jon Lock
Art by Ash Jackson, Jack Tempest, Sean McSorley, Grant Perkins,
Jack Davies, Jade Sarson, Mark Pearce, Warwick Fraser-Coombe,
Will Tempest and Nadine Ashworth
Letters by Michael Stock (with the exception of Pages 71-78)
Book design by Michael Stock
Cover art by Ash Jackson
Back cover art by Jack Tempest

First edition. Second printing: May 2013

For more about Afterlife Inc. and Jon's other works visit www.jonlock.com

What did you think of this book? Please email any feedback to
jonathanlock@btinternet.com. We look forward to hearing from you.

Connect with the world of Afterlife Inc.!
Follow on Facebook: www.facebook.com/jonlockcomics
Twitter feed: www.twitter.com/jonlockcomics

CONTENTS

AND SO WE ARRIVE AT THE DIFFICULT SECOND ALBUM...

Older, if not wiser; better travelled, if in no way closer to the final destination; and dogged by the worrying assumption that I somehow know what I'm doing.

I am indebted to the many artists, both new and returning, whose work features in this volume, and whose remarkable talent I am more than happy to exploit for my nefarious purposes.

To Ash and Jack, thank you for continuing to define the look and feel of AFTERLIFE INC. and for breathing life into a world I love. To Jade, Mark, Warwick, Grant, Nadine, Jack (Davies), Will and Sean – arguably the greatest team-up in comics history – thank you for ensuring that the afterlife never looked anything short of stupendous.

And if the only thing better than cake is surprise cake, then a special shout out has to be given to David, Travis and Nikki, whose awesome – and frankly unexpected – AFTERLIFE INC. fan art can be found in the Special Features section.

Massive thanks go to Michael Stock, for his immaculate lettering, not to mention the logo and design work on the book. This could well have been just a boring page of plain text. The fact that it is instead a rich feast for the senses speaks volumes.

On the technical front, Stu Gould of UK Comics is again responsible for bringing AFTERLIFE INC. from the screen onto the page with great aplomb and care. Matt Francis, web designer extraordinaire, not only keeps www.jonlock.com ticking over nicely, but recently helped recover the site from a devastating hack attack. (Cheers Matt!)

And, of course, who could forget the true stars of the show: the people, who, simply through kind words, shared drinks and good company, provide the emotional foundations on which this structure rests. Jess, John-Paul, Sally, Lynsey, Roy, Joe, Rachael, Mike, James, Steve, Kaytie, Paddy, Zach, Ben... con friends both new and old... Nich and Ali... the usual suspects back home... my family... (you know who you are). Thanks for making this so rewarding.

And to Lucy, my number one partner in crime, thanks for the love, friendship and – probably, above all – patience. You are wonderful.

Right, that's enough gushing praise for now. Go read the book, already, while I work on something interesting to say for Volume 3!

Jon Lock
Cheltenham 2012

NEAR LIFE
Chapter 1

Art by Ash Jackson

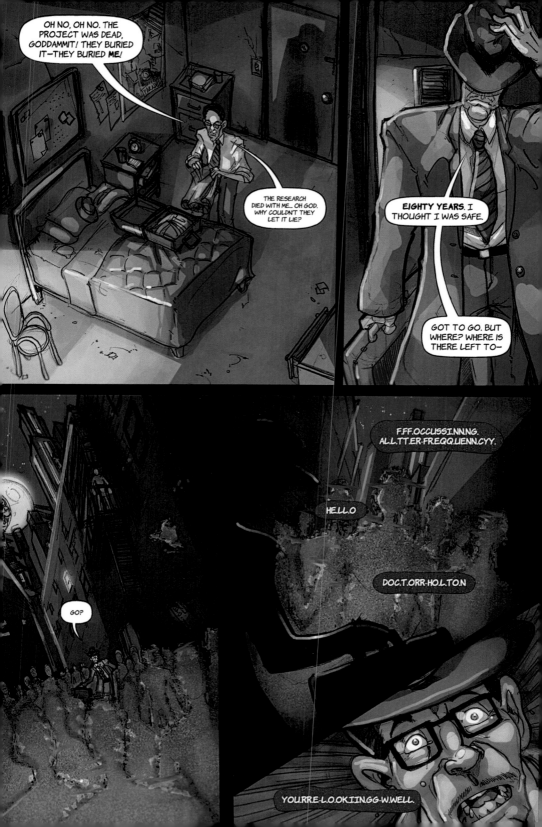

NEAR LIFE
Chapter 2

Art by Ash Jackson

NEAR LIFE
Chapter 3

Art by Ash Jackson

NEAR LIFE
Chapter 4

Art by Ash Jackson

DEAD DAYS

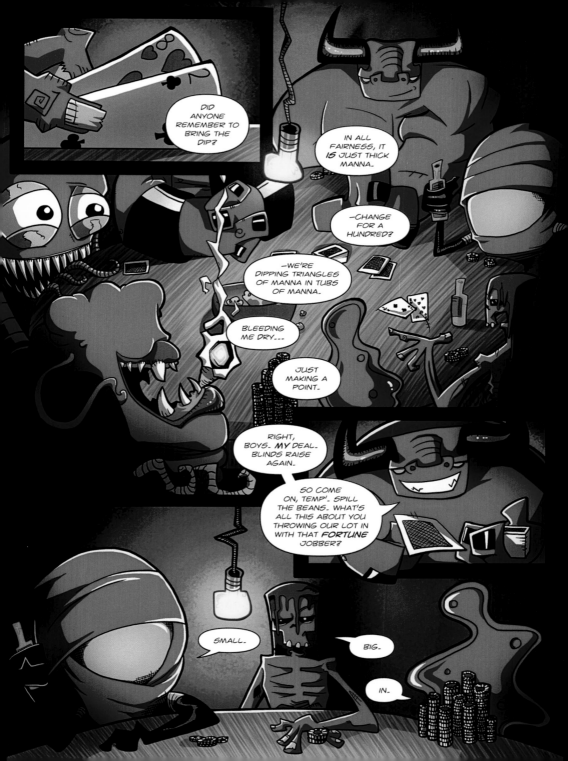

FIN.

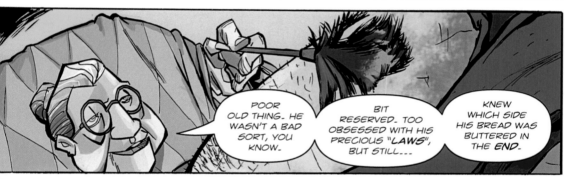

YOU DON'T... MIND THIS?

MIND, DEAR? WHY ON EARTH WOULD I MIND? DOES US GOOD TO HAVE A LITTLE LIFE AROUND THE PLACE.

THESE KIDS HAVE ETERNITY AHEAD OF THEM. MIGHT AS WELL ENJOY IT.

BEFORE... WHEN YOU SAID "SNUFFED IT." WHAT DID YOU MEAN? CASSIEL WAS AN ANGEL. HOW COULD HE DIE?

ARCHANGEL, DEAR. AND NO, CASSIEL'S NOT DEAD. JUST GONE. INERT.

HARD TO KILL WHAT WASN'T REALLY ALIVE IN THE FIRST PLACE.

JUST AS WELL REALLY.

TALKING TO DEAD PEOPLE IN THE DARK CAN'T BE ALL THAT HEALTHY...

AH, HERE WE GO. SEEING AS YOU'RE THE NEW BOSS AROUND HERE, I THOUGHT YOU MIGHT WANT TO SEE THIS.

CAREFUL NOW, DEAR. YOU MAY NEED A STRONG STOMACH.

THE WAIT

Art by Sean McSorley

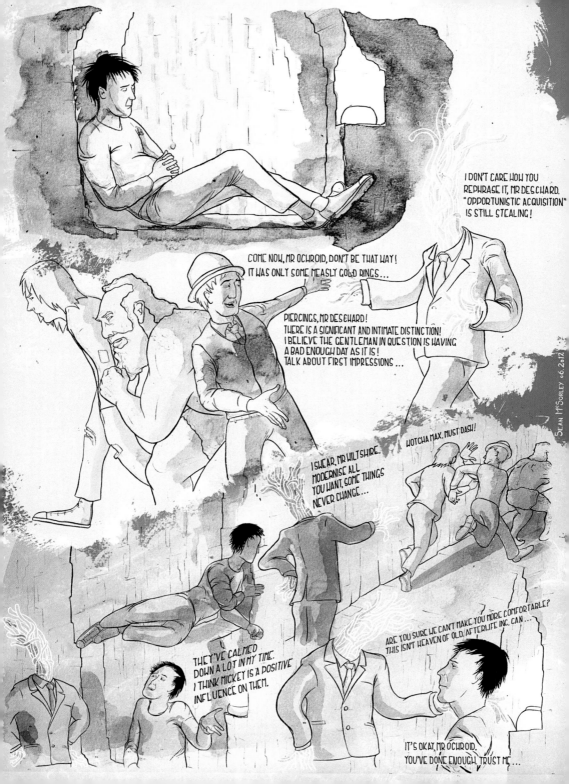

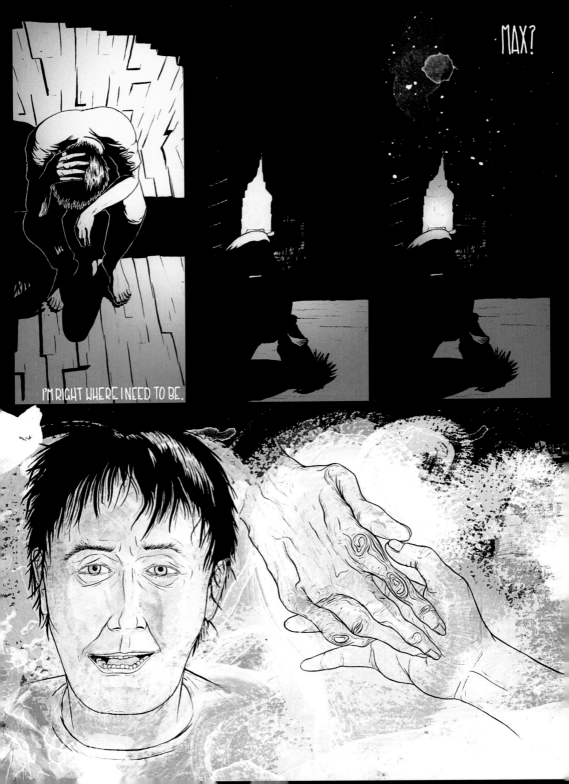

LAIKA

Art by Ash Jackson

SPECIAL FEATURES

PROFILE:
THE CALAMITY

The Calamity: destruction on a scale so
vast it requires Capitalisation.

Just who – or what – was responsible for the
devastating event that wiped the afterlife's ruling
body from existence and shook heaven to its core?

No-one knows. Or if they do, no-one's telling. But for
Jack and his company, whose meteoric rise to power
hinged so heavily on the chaos in the aftermath
of the Calamity, this at least is convenient.

Very convenient indeed.

Art by Ash Jackson

PROFILE:
THE STOOGES

Every society has them. Meet the Stooges a.k.a. Ronan Deschard and Associates, Finders and Seekers par excellence.

Whatever you want, whatever you need... whatever you can *afford*, these jacks-of-all-trades are your men.

Merging ineptitude, inebriation and an almost supernatural knack for self-preservation, Ronan and his two employees/drinking buddies (grunge kid Mickey and Neanderthal Harnk) eke out an existence as dealers in goods of "dubious origin".

Wherever there's a quick buck to be made – and few questions to be answered – the Stooges will never be far away.

Art by Ash Jackson

PROFILE:
MANNA

Direct from the gardens of Shehaqim! Fresh
manna, just the way you like it!

Feeling blue? Confused? Fatigued? Dehydrated? Hungry?

Existentially challenged?

We've got the cure for what ails you!

Sure the demand for food or drink died with our
bodies, but that's not to say the dead don't have
needs. Keep your manifestation solid and your
mind intact! Get some manna down you!

You wouldn't want to *dematerialise* now, would you?

"Manna. Lifts you up. *Keeps you anchored.*"

Art by Ash Jackson

GENESIS

Art by Jack Tempest

NO.

HOW COULD THIS HAVE COME TO PASS?

IT HAS EVER BEEN AS THUS.